CW00664473

Alex
PEATTIE + TAYLOR

Mandarin

To Ed

A Mandarin Paperback

ALEX

First published 1987 by Heinemann Kingswood
This edition published 1989 by Mandarin Paperbacks
Michelin House, 81 Fulham Road, London SW3 6RB

Mandarin is an imprint of the Octopus Publishing Group

ISBN 0 7493 0251 8

A CIP catalogue record for this title
is available from the British Library

Printed in Great Britain
by St Edmundsbury Press Ltd
Bury St Edmunds, Suffolk

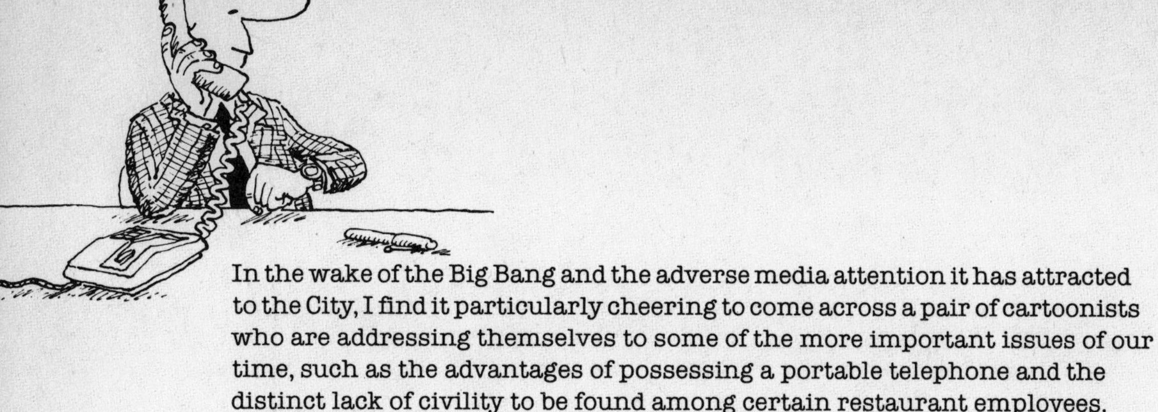

In the wake of the Big Bang and the adverse media attention it has attracted to the City, I find it particularly cheering to come across a pair of cartoonists who are addressing themselves to some of the more important issues of our time, such as the advantages of possessing a portable telephone and the distinct lack of civility to be found among certain restaurant employees.

Of course due to the inevitable limitations of the cartoon strip format we miss out on certain dimensions of the central character's life. I for one would like to have seen more of the inside of his car and of his bathroom (which I understand is furnished with some rather attractive antique taps and a powerful variable-jet shower). It seems remarkable too that on closing the book we still do not know exactly how many credit cards he carries (24, actually, not including Diners Club).

Lastly, I must apologise for the brevity of this foreword which is due entirely to the indifferent quality of the lunch provided for me by the two creators.

Yours sincerely,

Alex

Alex
PEATTIE + TAYLOR
I'M TWENTY FIVE AND I PULL IN FORTY THOUSAND A YEAR...
I HAVE AN EXCELLENT JOB, AN EXPENSIVE CAR AND A SUPERB FLAT ON A THREE PER CENT MORTGAGE...
BUT I'M NOT ALWAYS HAPPY. SOMETIMES I ASK MYSELF: WHAT DOES IT ALL MEAN?
MAYBE I SHOULD ASK FOR A RISE...

Alex
PEATTIE + TAYLOR
HEY, I JUST DUMPED A LOAD OF RUBBISH ON PIGSON AT METRO BANK.
002

BOY IS HE GOING TO BE MAD WHEN HE FINDS OUT WHAT HE'S BOUGHT.

ISN'T PIGSON THAT FRIEND OF YOURS IN FUTURES?

RIGHT GUY. WRONG TENSES.
Peattie

Alex
PEATTIE + TAYLOR
PAW
PAW
Peattie 003
I'M IN A
BULLISH MOOD
TODAY.

Alex
PEATTIE + TAYLOR
SIGH

...BLESS ME...
..WELL I NEVER...

WHAT? HMMMM?
OH THAT'S SWEET.

BANK STATEMENT.
OH.

Alex
PEATTIE + TAYLOR
RING

YES?

I DON'T KNOW. MAYBE. I'LL SEE WHAT I CAN DO.

FRANKFURT?
NO. MOTHER WANTS ME TO GO HOME FOR THE WEEKEND.

Alex
PEATTIE + TAYLOR
OH NO.
BUT I'M TOO YOUNG TO GO BALD...
COMB FLICK
I'LL JUST HAVE TO LIE ABOUT MY AGE...
Peattie 006

Alex
PEATTIE + TAYLOR
I HAVE JUST BOUGHT PILE OF DUD YOKOMOTO SHARES...
Peattie

THIS IS GREAT LOSS OF FACE AND PERSONAL DISHONOUR. I SHALL COMMIT HARAKIRI.

YOW

I DIDN'T THINK I HAD ANY STAPLES LEFT IN THIS ONE.

Alex
PEATTIE + TAYLOR
FLICK

FLIPPOW

SIR?
I DON'T KNOW WHERE I'D BE WITHOUT MY CREDIT CARDS...
FLAP CRACKLE FLAP

Alex
BEATTIE + TAYLOR
WHAT A MORNING... MY EX-GIRLFRIEND CAME ROUND AT SIX TO TAKE HER STEREO BACK...

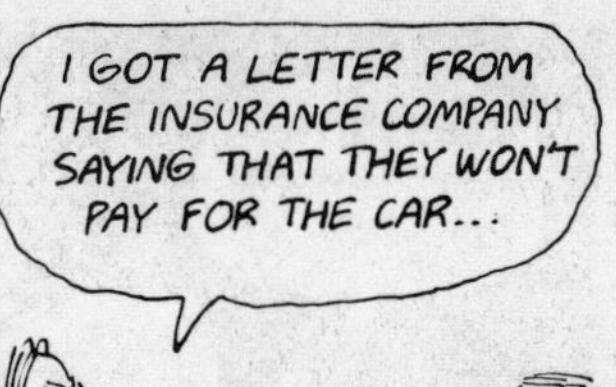
I GOT A LETTER FROM THE INSURANCE COMPANY SAYING THAT THEY WON'T PAY FOR THE CAR...

THE BANK IS TAKING AWAY MY GOLD CARD, AND TO TOP IT ALL...

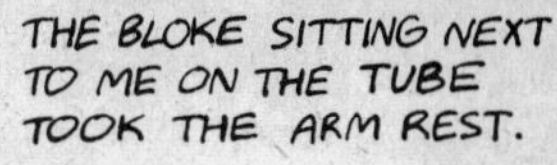
THE BLOKE SITTING NEXT TO ME ON THE TUBE TOOK THE ARM REST.

NASTY

Alex
PEATTIE+TAYLOR.
LOOK AT ALL THOSE STARS UP THERE..
OH YES.

THOUSANDS OF THEM... JUST THINK OF ALL THE PLANETS THERE MUST BE TOO...
010

DOESN'T IT MAKE YOU FEEL INSIGNIFICANT?
NOT REALLY...

I MEAN, HOW MANY OTHER TWENTY-FIVE YEAR OLDS DO YOU THINK THERE ARE UP THERE WHO OWN A BRAND NEW B.M.W. ?
Peattie

Alex
PEATTIE + TAYLOR
HELLO?.... SAMARITANS?...
ER... MY NAME'S ALEX AND I MAKE FORTY THOUSAND A YEAR....
WELL, I'VE JUST HAD A CAR PHONE FITTED IN MY NEW BMW...
...I JUST THOUGHT YOU MIGHT LIKE TO HEAR SOME GOOD NEWS FOR A CHANGE.

Alex
PEATTIE + TAYLOR
FIFTY PEE FOR A CUP OF TEA, GUV?
GET A JOB YOU PARASITE
THIS IS MY JOB.
I AM REGISTERED AS A LIMITED BEGGING COMPANY WITH MYSELF AS SOLE DIRECTOR. I AM NOT A PARASITE. I AM A SMALL BUSINESS.
I EARNED THAT.
Peattie 012

BISCUIT-TIN -O-FAX

Alex
BEATTIE + TAYLOR
PETER! HELLO! I'VE GOT A LITTLE PROPOSITION HERE WHICH MIGHT INTEREST YOU. HOW ABOUT DISCUSSING IT OVER DINNER?
013

ER... WELL IN THAT CASE, WHY DON'T WE TALK ABOUT IT OVER LUNCH TODAY?

YOU CAN'T?... A SWIFT HALF IN THE WINE BAR?... NO?... I'LL TELL YOU WHAT...

I'LL BIKE A BOTTLE OF VODKA OVER TO YOU... YOU DRINK IT AND THEN CALL ME BACK...

Alex
PEATTIE + TAYLOR
YOU'RE IN EARLY TODAY ALEX.
GOOD GRIEF! COME AND HAVE A LOOK AT THE SCREEN.
LOOK WHAT'S HAPPENED TO THE MARK!
I DON'T REALLY UNDERSTAND THESE CURRENCY THINGS...
IT'S STILL IN EXACTLY THE SAME POSITION.
SO?
WELL YOU WERE SUPPOSED TO CLEAN IT OFF.
RUB RUB
PEATTIE 014

Alex
PEATTIE + TAYLOR
Peattie 015
HEY, GUESS WHAT I JUST DID.
WHAT?
I JUST SOLD FOUR HUNDRED U.K GILT FUTURES TO PROTHEROE AT METROBANK AT ONE ONE EIGHT AND TWENTY NINE THIRTY SECONDTHS AND THE MARKET PRICE IS TWENTY EIGHT THIRTY SECONDTHS!
YOU DIDN'T!
HA HA HA HA HA HA.
HO HO HA HO HO HA HA HA HO.
WE DO HAVE A LARK IN HERE DON'T WE?
OH YES.

Alex
PEATTIE + TAYLOR
WELL YOU KNOW I CAN'T ADVISE YOU TO BUY...
BUT OFF THE RECORD PIGSON, LET'S SAY I HAVE A VERY GOOD FEELING ABOUT THOSE YOKOMUSHI SHARES...
DO YOU REALLY HAVE A GOOD FEELING ABOUT YOKOMUSHI, ALEX?
YUP. THEY'RE GOING THROUGH THE FLOOR TOMORROW AND I DON'T HAVE ANY.

Alex
PEATTIE + TAYLOR
I DON'T CARE TOO MUCH FOR MONEY ♫ COS MONEY CAN'T BUY ME LOVE.
TWING CLANG
CAN'T BUY ME LOVE MONEY CAN'T BUY ME LOVE ♫
PING DUNG
Peattie 017
HOW WOULD YOU KNOW, PAUPER?

Alex
BEATTIE + TAYLOR
YOU SHOULD STOP SMOKING ALEX.
YOU COULD TAKE UP SOMETHING ELSE, LIKE CHEWING-GUM.
Peattie 018
IT'S NOT THE SAME THOUGH IS IT?
CLICK
I MEAN, WHO EVER HEARD OF A SOLID GOLD MONOGRAMMED CHEWING GUM LIGHTER?

Alex
PEATTIE + TAYLOR
NO THANKS.

NO WAY. I'M NOT WEARING THAT.
Peattie 019

FORGET IT.

BYE MUMMY.
CLICK

Alex
PEATTIE + TAYLOR
THIS PICTURE, PENNY... I DON'T UNDERSTAND IT...
IT'S JUST A MASS OF COLOUR TO ME... DOES IT HAVE A TITLE?
IT'S CALLED: "TRIUMPH OF THE JAPANESE EQUITY WARRANT."
Peattie 020

Alex
PEATTIE + TAYLOR
... BUT OPERATOR, YOU HAVE TO LIST ME IN THE BOOK....
YOU CAN'T LIST A NUMBER WITHOUT THE SUBSCRIBERS ADDRESS...
I APPRECIATE THAT, SIR...
BUT AN ICE BLUE D REG. BMW 735 IS NOT A PROPER ADDRESS.
Peattie 021

Alex
BEATTIE + TAYLOR
I WOULD HAVE SAID FIFTY AT LEAST.
I'M TELLING YOU, HE'S ONLY THIRTY...
BUT HE'S GOT A HUGE PAUNCH, HIS HAIR'S FALLING OUT, HIS FACE IS COVERED IN WRINKLES...
I'M TELLING YOU... NO MORE THAN THIRTY.
FORTY?
THIRTY THOUSAND, THAT'S ALL HE EARNS.
STILL, THAT'S NOT BAD FOR A TWENTY FOUR YEAR OLD...

Alex
BEATTIE + TAYLOR
SIR?
OH ER... RARE PLEASE.

Peattie 023.
YES. RARE FOR ME TOO.
VERY RARE.

RIGHT, SO THAT'S THREE MIXED GRILLS OF ENDANGERED SPECIES...

Alex
BEATTIE + TAYLOR
OH NO. NOT ANOTHER SIX BILLION PAGE MANUAL ABOUT AVOIDING INSIDER TRADING...
INSIDER TRADING
I WISH THEY'D STOP GIVING US THESE THINGS...
WRAP WRAP
SELOTAPE
I MEAN, WHO GETS THE TIME TO READ SOMETHING LIKE THIS?
HELLO? CAROLINE? I'VE GOT AN AIR MAIL PACKAGE HERE FOR A MISTER I. BOESKY, CARE OF THE SECURITIES EXCHANGE COMMISSION...
Peattie 024.

Alex
PEATTIE + TAYLOR
IT'S FUNNY THAT I SHOULD END UP WITH A DESK JOB IN A CORPORATE FINANCE DEPARTMENT...

BECAUSE WHEN I WAS A NIPPER, WHAT I REALLY WANTED TO BE...

WAS A PRIMARY MARKET SYNDICATION EXECUTIVE...
ZZZ.

Alex
OH! SO YOU'RE A DANCER? THAT IS INTERESTING. I BET YOU KEEP FIT!

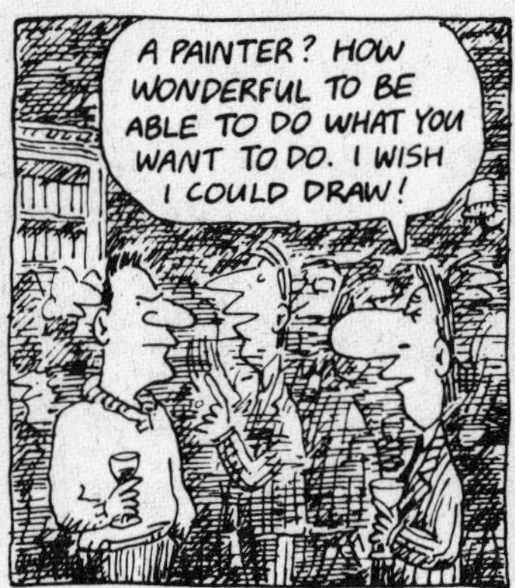
A PAINTER? HOW WONDERFUL TO BE ABLE TO DO WHAT YOU WANT TO DO. I WISH I COULD DRAW!

A WRITER? HOW MARVELLOUS! DO YOU WRITE ABOUT PEOPLE YOU KNOW?

I LOVE PATRONISING THE ARTS.

Alex
PEATTIE + TAYLOR
HELLO. MAY I SPEAK TO JUSTIN PARKER-JONES PLEASE?
I'M SORRY SIR, BUT HE'S ON ANOTHER LINE AT THE MOMENT...
Peattie 027.

Alex
BEATTIE + TAYLOR
HELLO. HOW'S BUSINESS?
BUSY. VERY BUSY.
I DECIDED TO DIVERSIFY MY INTERESTS.
DO YOU WANT TO BUY A BOX OF MATCHES?
I'LL GET BACK TO YOU.

Alex
WHAT'S THIS ALEX?
AH... THERE'S RATHER AN INTERESTING STORY BEHIND THAT...

PENNY AND I WERE DOWN IN THE SOUTH OF FRANCE AND WE HAPPENED TO MEET DAVID HOCKNEY IN A RESTAURANT...

AND HE STARTED DOODLING ON A TABLE NAPKIN...

AND I TOOK THIS PICTURE OF HIM BEING SHOUTED AT BY THE PROPRIETOR.

Alex
PEATTIE + TAYLOR
A TAKEOVER? SORRY PETER, THAT'S NOT A MATTER I CAN COMMENT ON AT THE MOMENT.
Peattie 030.
SORRY BRIAN... I'M GOING TO HAVE TO DODGE THAT ONE...
ALEX, YOU'VE SET THE WHOLE CITY BUZZING WITH RUMOURS.
I'M AWARE OF THAT.
BUT IT'S SO UNPROFESSIONAL TO ADMIT YOU DON'T KNOW.
RING RING

Alex
PEATTIE + TAYLOR
YOUR BILL, SIR.

WHAT?
Peattie032.

OH MY GOD!

IS THAT ALL?
PLEASE STOP SHOWING OFF.

Alex
PEATTIE + TAYLOR
HI-FI
AH YES... NOW THIS IS A VERY SUPERIOR SYSTEM SIR...
SMALL PANEL HERE IS TOUCH SENSITIVE CONTROLS, COMPACT QUADRAPHONIC SPEAKERS, SEPARATE SHALLOW UNITS TOPPED WITH THIS ELEGANT LOW PROFILE SMOKED GLASS COVER...
..AND AS YOU CAN SEE, IT COMES DESIGN CO-ORDINATED IN A SMOOTH HI-TECH MATT BLACK FINISH..
HMMM...
ACTUALLY I WAS LOOKING FOR SOMETHING A BIT MORE OSTENTATIOUS.

Alex
PEATTIE + TAYLOR
BYE.
EXCUSE ME...
MAY I BORROW YOUR PHONE FOR A MOMENT? ...I'M RATHER ANXIOUS TO REACH SOMEONE...
CERTAINLY.
CLIVE! I THOUGHT IT WAS YOU!
OH. HELLO.
TAP TAP

Alex
PEATTIE + TAYLOR
IT'S MR NAKOBUSHI FROM FIRST SAKAMOTO BANK...
PEATTIE 034.
HE SAYS HE'S SHORT ON GILTS...
TELL HIM: WHAT ABOUT PEARL HARBOR? WHAT ABOUT THE BRITISH CAR INDUSTRY?
AND IF THAT DOESN'T MAKE HIM FEEL BAD, ASK HIM: HOW ABOUT BIRDS NEST SOUP?

Alex
PEATTIE + TAYLOR
WHAT DO YOU THINK OF THIS PAINTING, ALEX?
IT LOOKS LIKE A LOAD OF OLD RUBBISH TO ME, RUPERT.

THIS IS ACTUALLY YOUR NEW OFFICE PAINTING, ALEX.
OH.

AND IT'S A MASTERPIECE OF THE HAROSIKI DISRUPTIVIST SCHOOL ... I CAN REVEAL THAT THE BOARD PAID OVER £15,000 FOR IT.
Peattie 035

...LET THAT BE A LESSON TO YOU ALEX. NEVER JUDGE BY APPEARANCES.
SORRY RUPERT.

Alex
PEATTIE + TAYLOR
I SPEND A LOT OF TIME TRAVELLING TO DIFFERENT PARTS OF THE WORLD ON BUSINESS...
AND SOMETIMES I FEEL QUITE DEPRESSED BY THE DEPRIVATIONS AND SOCIAL INJUSTICES WHICH I ENCOUNTER...
I MEAN, HERE'S ME... I'M TWENTY FIVE, I ENJOY AN AFFLUENT LIFESTYLE, I HAVE A WELL PAID JOB IN A MERCHANT BANK...
AND MY STINGY FIRM WON'T EVEN PAY FOR ME TO TRAVEL BY CONCORDE...
ZZZ

Alex
PEATTIE + TAYLOR
I WAS THINKING, PENNY, WHY NOT WEAR YOUR BLUE SILK COCKTAIL DRESS TONIGHT?
WHY?
WELL, I'VE GOT A LITTLE SURPRISE FOR YOU....
WHICH WOULD GO NICELY WITH THAT BLUE DRESS...
NEW CAR SEAT COVERS. HOW ROMANTIC.

Alex
TWO BURGERS WITH FRENCH FRIES AND SIDE SALADS.

EXCUSE ME... COULD WE HAVE SOME RELISH?

Peattie 038
YEAH OKAY.

HERE YOU ARE TWO JUICY CHARCOAL GRILLED BURGERS WITH DELICIOUS YUMMY FRENCH FRIES AND FRESH CRISP SALADS IN A SPECIAL SAUCE. MM, MMMM!
THAT'S MORE LIKE IT.

Alex
BEATTIE + TAYLOR
WHEN YOU'RE INVOLVED IN CHARITY WORK ONE HEARS QUITE A LOT OF CRITICISM ABOUT THESE PARTIES...

PEOPLE SEEM TO FORGET THE IMPORTANCE OF THESE FUNCTIONS AS FUND-RAISING OPERATIONS..

YOU'VE JUST GOT TO HAVE THE BALLS TO RAISE MONEY.
YUP.

YOU GOTTA KICK PLENTY OF ASS TOO.

Alex
PEATTIE + TAYLOR
BLESS ME.
CLIVE, DO YOU KNOW WHAT THE USUAL PRISON TERM IS FOR SOMEONE CONVICTED OF INSIDER DEALING?
INSIDER TRADING
NO... WHAT?
A "TOFFEE-NOSED GIT."
INSIDER TRADING

Alex
PEATTIE + TAYLOR
IGNORE THOSE RUMOURS SIMON, THESE BONDS ARE AN EXCELLENT INVESTMENT.... YOU HAVE MY WORD ON THAT...
FINE, ... NICE DOING BUSINESS WITH YOU.
CLICK
IS THAT TRUE?
CLIVE! MY WORD IS MY BOND.
AND NEITHER OF THEM IS WORTH A TOOT.

Alex
PEATTIE + TAYLOR
...ALEX AND I STAYED IN THIS HOTEL ON THE CHAMPS ELYSEES. BREAKFAST COST TWO HUNDRED AND FIFTY FRANCS...AND THAT WAS JUST FOR A CUP OF COFFEE AND A CROISSANT!
OH NO. WHAT A RIP-OFF.
&Co.

... ANYWAY, PENNY AND I STAYED IN THIS HOTEL ON THE CHAMPS ELYSEES. BREAKFAST COST TWO HUNDRED AND FIFTY FRANCS... AND THAT WAS JUST FOR A CUP OF COFFEE AND A CROISSANT.
WOW! CAN YOU GIVE ME THE ADDRESS?

Alex
HELLO? MR GREEN?... I THINK I MAY HAVE FOUND SOMETHING THAT BELONGS TO YOU...

YES... ONE RATHER TATTY WALLET, NO CREDIT CARDS, FIVE POUNDS IN CASH...

DO YOU WANT IT BACK?

Alex
GIVE ME THE BILL. I'LL WORK IT OUT.
IT'S OKAY I'M NEARLY THERE.
GIVE HIM THE BILL, ALEX. HE'S GOT A CALCULATOR.
THAT'S NOT A CALCULATOR.
ULP.
THIS IS A CALCULATOR.
GLEAM
GLEAM
HE SAW "CROCODILE DUNDEE" FIVE TIMES, YOU KNOW.
CORKS!

Alex
PEATTIE + TAYLOR
HELLO MATE.
GOT ANY SPARE CHANGE?
CATCH.
Peattie 045.

Alex
BEATTIE + TAYLOR
LAST YEAR PENNY AND I STAYED IN THIS SUPER LITTLE VILLAGE ON ONE OF THE GREEK ISLANDS. ... COMPLETELY UNSPOILT...
IT'S AS IF NOTHING HAS CHANGED THERE IN HUNDREDS OF YEARS...
THE LOCAL PEOPLE STILL KEEP UP ALL THEIR OLD CUSTOMS AND TRADITIONS...
DO YOU KNOW, THEY STILL TUG THEIR FORELOCKS AS YOU DRIVE PAST....?
HOW MARVELLOUS!

Alex
BEATTIE + TAYLOR
TALKING OF EMBARRASSING MOMENTS... I WAS ON THE TUBE THE OTHER DAY...
...AND I DROPPED MY NEW BRIEFCASE AND IT BURST OPEN... IT WAS SO EMBARRASSING...
WHY? WHAT WAS IN IT?
NOTHING.
CRINGE

Alex
BEATTIE + TAYLOR
SO, LET'S GET THIS STRAIGHT SIR... THEY TOOK ALL YOUR CASH..?
ONE POUND THIRTY SEVEN PEE...
BUT THEY DIDN'T TAKE ANY OF YOUR CREDIT CARDS OR OTHER VALUABLES?
THAT'S RIGHT.
DID THEY THREATEN YOU IN ANY WAY?
THEY WERE EXTREMELY ABUSIVE...
WELL I'M SORRY SIR, BUT REFUSING TO ACCEPT A MAJOR CREDIT CARD AS PAYMENT FOR A CHINESE MEAL IS NOT A CRIMINAL OFFENCE.
YOU MEAN YOU'RE GOING TO LET THEM GET AWAY WITH IT?

Alex
BEATTIE + TAYLOR
DOES ANYONE HERE OWN A BLUE BMW? BECAUSE IT'S BLOCKING ACCESS TO THE CAR PARK...
I REPEAT: WOULD THE OWNER OF A POWDER BLUE BMW 735, REGISTRATION NUMBER D007 AL...
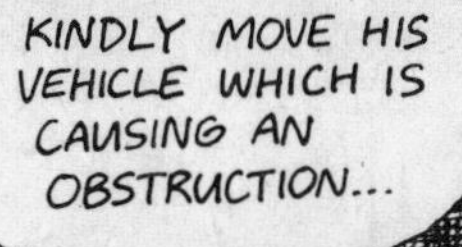
KINDLY MOVE HIS VEHICLE WHICH IS CAUSING AN OBSTRUCTION...

COME ON ALEX. GET UP.

ONCE AGAIN: WHOEVER IT IS WHO OWNS THE FOUR DOOR, POWDER BLUE....
JUST WAIT TILL HE GETS TO THE POWER STEERING...

Alex
BEATTIE + TAYLOR
HA HA HA...
SAY NO
MORE!
Peattie 050.

RIGHT!
HA HA...
MUM'S THE
WORD...

OKAY PETER,
A NOD'S AS
GOOD AS A
WINK...

I'M AFRAID
I'M GOING TO
HAVE TO ASK
YOU TO
SHUT UP
NOW...

Alex
PEATTIE + TAYLOR
SO, WHAT DO YOU THINK OF THE NEW COMPANY LIMOUSINE, ALEX?

ACTUALLY RUPERT, I THINK SOME OF THESE GIMMICKS ARE A BIT POINTLESS...
REALLY?

WHEN I'M BEING DRIVEN THROUGH TOWN IN A BIG EXPENSIVE CAR, FRANKLY THE LAST THING I NEED...

IS SMOKED-GLASS WINDOWS.

Alex
PEATTIE + TAYLOR
I'M FAIRLY CONFIDENT ABOUT MY LONG TERM FUTURE... I HAVE A NUMBER OF OPTIONS TO CONSIDER IN THE SHORT TERM... MY ANALYSIS IS HELPING ME DEAL WITH SOME GUILTS... ... I'M THINKING OF GETTING INTO ZEN...

TISH
TISH
MAG
I'M FAIRLY CONFIDENT ABOUT MY LONG TERM FUTURES... I HAVE A NUMBER OF SHORT TERM OPTIONS TO CONSIDER... MY ANALYST IS HELPING ME DEAL IN SOME GILTS.... ..I'M THINKING OF GETTING INTO YEN....

Alex
PEATTIE + TAYLOR
WOW! BIG SHAKE-UP AT METROBANK... PARKINSON HAS BEEN TOLD TO CONSIDER HIMSELF ON INDEFINITE SUSPENSION WITHOUT PAY...
Peattie 053
AND HODGE-BROWN AND JARVIS WERE INVITED TO TENDER THEIR RESIGNATIONS...

PROTHEROE HAS BEEN REQUESTED TO MAKE ARRANGEMENTS TO SEEK AN ALTERNATIVE SITUATION...

AND PERKINS WAS TOLD HE WAS SACKED...
OH YES. HE'S THE THICK ONE ISN'T HE?

Alex
Customs Hall
THAT WAS EXTREMELY EMBARRASSING.
THEY WERE ONLY DOING THEIR JOB CLIVE...
YES, BUT THEY DIDN'T HAVE TO HUMILIATE ME IN FRONT OF ALL THE OTHER PASSENGERS...
THE POINT IS, CUSTOMS OFFICERS KNOW THAT IT IS USUALLY THE CLEAN-CUT AND RESPECTABLE-LOOKING PASSENGERS...
WHO HAVE THE MOST EMBARRASSING PASSPORT PHOTOGRAPHS..
BUT LONG HAIR WAS FASHIONABLE THEN...

TIPPEX

Alex
BEATTIE + TAYLOR
I'LL BE GETTING A RISE IN THREE MONTHS...

AND I'LL BE PROMOTED WITHIN ABOUT A YEAR.
OH.

AND I'LL BE A MILLIONAIRE BY THE TIME I'M THIRTY FIVE.

GIPSY FORTUNE TELLER →
HAVEN'T WE GOT THIS THE WRONG WAY ROUND?

Alex
PEATTIE + TAYLOR
Peattie 056
I THINK WHAT I VALUE ABOVE ALL ELSE AT THIS PLACE....
JUST ONE MINUTE SIR WHILE I WRAP IT UP FOR YOU...
IS THE OLD-FASHIONED CIVILITY OF THE SERVICE...
HERE YOU ARE SIR.
THEY NEVER FORGET THAT COURTESY COSTS YOU NOTHING...
THANKYOU VERY MUCH SIR. HOPE TO SEE YOU AGAIN SOON.
THE BLATANT TOADYING WORKS OUT AT ABOUT FORTY QUID A SHIRT THOUGH...

Alex
PEATTIE + TAYLOR
HELLO? CLIVE SPEAKING... OH HELLO ALEX...

PARTY NEXT SATURDAY? YES I CAN MAKE THAT.... THANKS WHAT ARE YOU CELEBRATING? IT'S NOT YOUR BIRTHDAY?...

OH.

I'VE NEVER BEEN TO A CREDIT LIMIT EXTENSION PARTY BEFORE...

WELL DONE
CONGRAT ULATIONS

Alex
BEATTIE + TAYLOR
ALEX... THE BUCK STOPS HERE.
EXECUTIVE DIRECTOR
RUPERT, I SAY THAT AT THE END OF THE DAY IT STOPS HERE...
DOLLAR/YEN
OKAY, TWO BOTTLES OF CHAMPAGNE IT STOPS DOWN HERE...

Alex
BEATTIE + TAYLOR
HOW'S THAT FLOTATION GOING?

CAN WE TALK ABOUT THAT SOME OTHER TIME PETER? I PREFER NOT TO MIX BUSINESS WITH PLEASURE.

OF COURSE... SURE... SO, HOW ARE THINGS AT HOME?

OH NOT BAD... I DID QUITE NICELY OUT OF MY B.A. SHARES....

Alex
BEATTIE + TAYLOR
BUSY AT THE MOMENT?
YUP. LOT ON THE HORIZON.
THANKYOU.

I'M THINKING OF GETTING A MOUTH ORGAN. WHAT DO YOU RECKON?...
MAYBE... ER.. ACTUALLY NO. I DON'T THINK SO.
THANKYOU.

OI!
THANKYOU

CONSULTANCY FEE.

Alex
PEATTIE + TAYLOR
I WISH YOU WOULDN'T WEAR THAT AWFUL FAKE LACOSTE SHIRT...

..AND THAT OBVIOUS CHEAP COPY OF A CARTIER WATCH...

I WOULD HAVE THOUGHT YOU COULD AFFORD THE REAL THING ANYWAY.
Peattie 061

YES... BUT THEN HOW WOULD PEOPLE GUESS I'D BEEN TO THAILAND?

Alex
BEATTIE + TAYLOR
ALRIGHT CLIVE, LONDON MARATHON MONEY. COUGH UP.

HOW MUCH WAS IT?
TEN QUID.

I TOLD YOU YOU WOULDN'T FINISH.

Alex
HMMM, WE'VE GOT AN INVITATION HERE TO DRINKS FROM OLIVIA FITZGIBBON...
OH THAT'S NICE.

I JUST DON'T KNOW IF WE CAN FIT IT IN THOUGH...

YOU COULD ALWAYS TAKE DOWN GUY AND FIONA'S WEDDING INVITATION. IT WAS TWO YEARS AGO...
YES. BUT THE RECEPTION WAS IN A STATELY HOME...

Alex
PEATTIE + TAYLOR
WHAT'LL YOU HAVE, PENNY?
OH A TOMATO JUICE, PLEASE.

COME ON... HAVE A PROPER DRINK... HAVE A HALF OF LAGER.
JUST A TOMATO JUICE PLEASE.

AT LEAST HAVE A DASH OF VODKA IN IT...
NO.
THE IDEA OF ME ACTUALLY PASSING MY DRIVING TEST THIS TIME REALLY FRIGHTENS YOU DOESN'T IT ALEX?
HIGHWAY CODE.

Alex
PEATTIE + TAYLOR
FUNNY... THERE'S NO ANSWER...
BRRR
BRRR
BRRR

I LENT PENNY THE CAR FOR HER DRIVING TEST....
BRRR
BRRR

AND I WANT TO FIND OUT HOW SHE GOT ON...
BRRR
BRR
BRRR

YES? WHAT?
D007 AL
L
CRUMP.

Alex
PEATTIE + TAYLOR
PLUNK
PLINK
THANKYOU GENTS.
SAVE THE CHILDREN

TO YOU AND ME CLIVE, FRANKLY THEY'RE JUST A NUISANCE...

BUT IT'S GOOD TO KNOW THAT SOMEBODY REALLY VALUES THEM...
CHILDREN?

NO... FIFTY PENCE PIECES.

Alex
PEATTIE+TAYLOR.
IT'S FUNNY TO THINK THAT AT TWENTY-FIVE I EARN MORE THAN MY DAD...

YOU KNOW, MY MOTHER STILL REMEMBERS THE DAY WHEN HE FOUND OUT THAT I EARNED MORE THAN HIM...
HOW DID HE REACT?

APPARENTLY HE TORE UP MY TELEGRAM...

Alex
BEATTIE + TAYLOR
YOU KNOW, YOU'LL PROBABLY BE THE ONLY LABOUR-VOTING SMALL BUSINESSMAN AT THE NEXT ELECTION...
I BEG YOUR PARDON. I'VE ALWAYS BEEN A VERY LOYAL ADMIRER OF MRS THATCHER.
I AGREE WITH TAXATION OF THE LOWER PAID... YOU HAVE TO HAVE SOME INCENTIVE TO WORK.
I SHALL BE ABLE TO TELL MY FRIENDS I'M IN A TAX BRACKET SOON.
ANYWAY I'M NOT SMALL.

Alex
BEATTIE + TAYLOR
WHEN I WAS A LAD IN THE THIRTIES, MY DAD HAD SIX OF US KIDS AND A WIFE TO SUPPORT WHEN HE GOT LAID OFF AT THE FOUNDRY...

BUT HE DIDN'T SIT AROUND GRUMBLING ABOUT BEING UNEMPLOYED...

HE GOT ON HIS BIKE AND WENT OFF LOOKING FOR WORK.
MATCHES

I OFTEN WONDER WHAT BECAME OF HIM...
MATCHES

Z
SHARE APPLICATION
SHARE APPLICATION
SHARE APPLICATION
SHARE

Alex
PEATTIE + TAYLOR
I JUST HAD LUNCH WITH SIR ROLAND...YES I THINK HE FOUND YOUR COMPANY FIGURES QUITE PERSUASIVE...
Peattie 070.

HOWEVER HE'S STILL CONCERNED ABOUT THE LEVEL OF APRECIATION ON HIS INVESTMENT.

I THINK HE'D LIKE TO SEE A THOROUGH BREAKDOWN FROM YOUR FINANCIAL DIRECTOR AT THE MEETING TOMORROW...

BUT BETWEEN YOU AND ME, A LITTLE WHIMPERING WOULD PROBABLY SATISFY HIM.

Alex
PEATTIE + TAYLOR
RING RING
EXCUSE ME EVERYONE..

ALEX! HELLO! WE WERE WONDERING WHAT HAD HAPPENED TO YOU... AH, YOU'RE ON YOUR ROMAFONE...

WHAT?... OKAY... YOU HOLD ON THERE... I'LL GET ONTO IT STRAIGHT AWAY...

APPARENTLY THERE'S NO PAPER IN THE TOILET.

Alex
PEATTIE + TAYLOR
ALEX, I WONDER IF YOU COULD HAVE A FEW WORDS WITH YOUNG PRENTISS...

I DON'T WANT TO HAVE TO SPEAK TO HIM MYSELF BUT HIS LUNCHTIME DRINKING HABITS HAVE BECOME SOMETHING OF A TALKING POINT...

EITHER HE SHAPES UP OR HE'LL HAVE TO START LOOKING FOR ALTERNATIVE EMPLOYMENT...

MALIBU AND PINEAPPLE DOES NOT SUIT OUR CORPORATE IMAGE.
LEAVE IT TO ME RUPERT.

Alex
BEATTIE + TAYLOR
WELL I'M SERIOUSLY WORRIED ABOUT THE RESULT OF THIS NEXT ELECTION...

SAY LABOUR DID GET IN... IT COULD BE THE END FOR PEOPLE LIKE YOU AND ME...

I SUPPOSE I MIGHT BE ABLE TO GET A JOB IN DENMARK...

BUT IT COULD BE REALLY TOUGH FOR YOU ALTERNATIVE COMEDIANS...

Alex
BEATTIE + TAYLOR
BUT ALEX, YOU HAVE TO UNDERSTAND THAT SOME PEOPLE IN THIS NEIGHBOURHOOD HAVE BEEN LIVING HERE FOR YEARS.

THIS USED TO BE QUITE A POOR AREA... THEY'VE SEEN IT GO UPMARKET... HOUSES CHANGING HANDS...

YOU'VE GOT TO EXPECT SOME RESENTMENT...

I DON'T RESENT THEM, PENNY. I JUST SAID SOME OF THEM WERE A BIT SCRUFFY.

Alex
PEATTIE + TAYLOR
SLIGHT HITCH IN THE DEAL, RUPERT. WE STILL CAN'T GET SIR ROLAND TO COME ROUND..

REMIND ME, ALEX, WHAT DID WE HAVE ON THE TABLE?
Peattie 075.

WE DIDN'T OFFER HIM ANYTHING OVER 12%..

12%? THAT DOESN'T SOUND EXCESSIVE...

NO, BUT HE DRANK THREE BOTTLES...
SIR ROLAND?

Alex
PEATTIE + TAYLOR
HOW DID YOU DO ON THE ROLLS ROYCE SHARE ISSUE?
OH ALRIGHT... NOTHING TO WRITE HOME ABOUT...

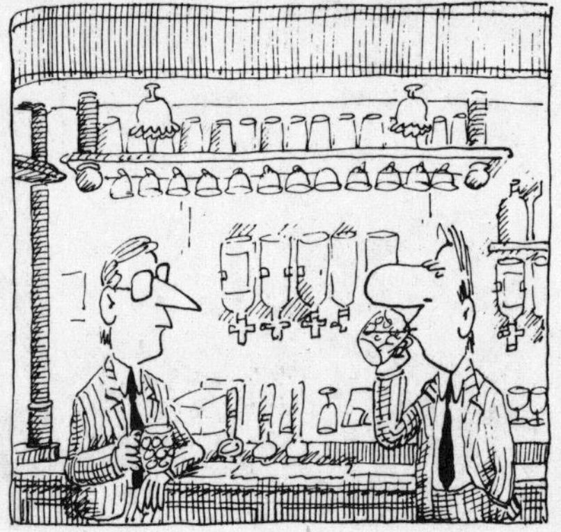

OR ANY OF THE OTHER SEVENTEEN ADDRESSES I USED ON MY APPLICATION FORMS...

Alex
PEATTIE + TAYLOR
ALEX, I REALLY THINK WE SHOULD GIVE FIONA'S DINNER PARTY A MISS.
MONEY

ALL THAT HAPPENS THESE DAYS IS YOU FALL ASLEEP STRAIGHT AFTER SUPPER ANYWAY...
MONEY

AND THEN I HAVE TO TELL EVERYONE HOW HARD YOU'VE BEEN WORKING SINCE YOUR PROMOTION, HOW MUCH WORK YOUR DEPARTMENT HAS ON AT THE MOMENT, HOW MANY LATE NIGHTS YOU'VE HAD AT THE OFFICE...

THEN YOU WAKE UP AND IT'S TIME TO GO HOME.
WELL, SOMETIMES YOU TELL THEM ABOUT ALL MY BREAKFAST MEETINGS WITH MY HEADHUNTER..
MONEY

Alex
PEATTIE + TAYLOR
SORRY I'M LATE PENNY.
YOU LOOK DREADFUL. I SUPPOSE THIS MEANS YOU'VE BEEN OUT WITH THE BOYS FROM METRO BANK AGAIN.

NONE OF YOU KNOW YOUR LIMITS DO YOU? WHAT ARE THESE SESSIONS SUPPOSED TO PROVE? IS IT SOME KIND OF TRIAL OF MACHISMO?
YOU SHOULD HAVE SEEN THE OTHERS.

APART FROM ANYTHING ELSE IT'S SUCH A WASTE OF MONEY...

I MEAN, YOU DON'T EVEN LIKE OPERA.
TANNHAUSER PROGRAMME

Alex
BEATTIE + TAYLOR
THEY ALL LOOK THE SAME TO ME...

THEY'RE TAKING OVER THE WHOLE NEIGHBOURHOOD..

YOU CAN SMELL THEIR COOKING ALL DOWN THE STREET... I'M NOT PREJUDICED OR ANYTHING...

... I MEAN, SOME OF MY BEST FRIENDS ARE SLOANE RANGERS..
ADVICE CENTRE
PIPPA! HI!
VIKKI! HI!
NIKKI! HI!
ZOE! HI!
PENNY! HI!
HI!

Alex
PEATTIE + TAYLOR
WHAT WERE YOU DRINKING, CLIVE?
PINT OF DIRECTORS PLEASE.

I'M HAVING ANOTHER GUINNESS... PETER?
PINT OF BITTER PLEASE, ALEX.

ER... BITTER, ... GUINNESS, ... DIRECTORS, PLEASE..
CLUNK
CLUNK

THEY'RE IN THE OTHER BAR SIR, HAVING A WHIP-ROUND FOR ERNIE SAUNDERS.

Alex
PEATTIE + TAYLOR
ACTUALLY PETER, IF WE'RE GOING TO DISCUSS CONFIDENTIAL FINANCIAL MATTERS WOULD YOU MIND IF WE MOVED TO ANOTHER TABLE?

WORRIED ABOUT BEING OVERHEARD?
MMM... YES...

COULDN'T WE JUST SPEAK UP A BIT?
I SUPPOSE SO...

NOW YOU WERE ASKING ME ABOUT MY SALARY...
COULD WE BE MOVED TO ANOTHER ROOM PLEASE, WAITER?...

Alex
PEATTIE + TAYLOR
ALEX, WHAT DO YOU THINK WOULD BE THE MOST REALISTIC POLICY FOR US TO ADOPT IN THE EVENT OF A NUCLEAR WAR?
SELL. EVERYTHING.

Alex
PEATTIE + TAYLOR
I WAS SO NERVOUS WHEN I FIRST MET ALEX'S PARENTS...

THIS MAY SOUND REALLY WEIRD BUT I JUST KEPT NEEDING TO GO TO THE TOILET...

ACTUALLY PENNY, THAT'S FAIRLY COMMON...

OH SORRY... I MEAN I KEPT NEEDING TO GO TO THE LOO...

Alex
PEATTIE + TAYLOR
WELL I DON'T REALLY CARE ABOUT LOOKS...

I SUPPOSE I GO MORE FOR SOMEONE WITH A SENSE OF HUMOUR... SOMEONE I CAN TALK TO...

I QUITE LIKE PEOPLE WHO ARE CREATIVE ...NOT TOO TRENDY... THEY HAVE TO BE SENSITIVE IF I'M GOING TO GET ON WITH THEM IN THE LONG TERM...

RIGHT, THAT'S ENOUGH ABOUT HAIRDRESSERS, NOW WHAT ABOUT BOYFRIENDS?
WELL I'VE ALWAYS THOUGHT A CAR WAS QUITE IMPORTANT...

Alex
PEATTIE + TAYLOR
CAN I GET YOU A DRINK, CLIVE? WHAT WOULD YOU LIKE?

WELL, WHAT HAVE YOU GOT?

...AND ER... RATHER A GOOD BARREL FERMENTED CHARDONNAY 1985 FROM CLOS DU BOIS... ER...

Alex
PEATTIE + TAYLOR
YOU SHOULD HAVE SEEN PIGSON AFTER LUNCH... HE WAS PRACTICALLY INCAPABLE...

WHEN I GOT HIM BACK TO METROBANK HE WAS SICK IN THE LIFT.

OH NO. WHO CLEANED UP?
I DID.

I SOLD HIM SOME MORE OF THOSE DUD DENMARK FUTURES...

Alex
PEATTIE + TAYLOR
TAJ
MAHAL
PHEW. I THINK I NEED ANOTHER GLASS OF WATER... I SHOULD NEVER HAVE LET YOU ORDER US BOTH VINDALOOS.

MY EYES ARE WATERING... MY NOSE IS RUNNING... I'M SWEATING ALL OVER...

MY STOMACH IS CHURNING SO MUCH I THINK I'M GOING TO BE SICK.

SHUT UP CLIVE, HE'S BRINGING THEM...
OOER.

Alex
PEATTIE + TAYLOR
YES, IT'LL HAVE TO BE A BREAKFAST MEETING THOUGH..

I'M PRETTY BUSY AT THE MOMENT... SHALL WE SAY WEDNESDAY WEEK?

7·15 OKAY BY YOU?... FINE.

SO YOU WANT TO GET NEW CURTAINS, PENNY?
ZZZZ

NEWS
BRITAIN VOTES TODAY
OLIVIA'S ELECTION NIGHT PARTY
RSVP
NIGEL & SARA'S ELECTION NIGHT PARTY
I STILL CANT DECIDE ON WHICH PARTY.

Alex
PEATTIE + TAYLOR
BLOODY BUREAUCRAT! WHAT EXACTLY DID HE SAY, CAROLINE?

HE SAID HE'S VERY SORRY BUT HE CAN'T HELP YOU...
DID YOU TELL HIM WHO I AM?

YES BUT HE SAID IT REALLY IS IMPOSSIBLE..

APPARENTLY THERE'S NO SUCH THING AS A TELEPHONE VOTE.
OKAY TELL HIM I'LL FAX IT OVER.

Alex
PEATTIE + TAYLOR
WINE BAR
HERE WE GO HERE WE GO HERE WE GO...
I SUPPOSE MRS THATCHER WILL JUST GO ON AND ON NOW...
WELL, SHE'S BOUND TO BE A BIT VERBOSE..